CHRISTMAS
TREASURY

The Twelve Days of Christmas

On the first day of Christmas
My true love sent to me
A partridge in a pear tree.

On the second day of Christmas
My true love sent to me
Two turtle doves
And a partridge in a pear tree.

On the third day of Christmas
My true love sent to me
Three French hens.

On the fourth day of Christmas
My true love sent to me
Four calling birds.

On the fifth day of Christmas
My true love sent to me
Five gold rings.

On the sixth day of Christmas
My true love sent to me
Six geese a-laying.

On the seventh day of Christmas
My true love sent to me
Seven swans a-swimming.

On the eighth day of Christmas
My true love sent to me
Eight maids a-milking.

On the ninth day of Christmas
My true love sent to me
Nine drummers drumming.

On the tenth day of Christmas
My true love sent to me
Ten pipers piping.

On the eleventh day of Christmas
My true love sent to me
Eleven ladies dancing.

On the twelfth day of Christmas
My true love sent to me
Twelve lords a-leaping,
Eleven ladies dancing,
Ten pipers piping,
Nine drummers drumming,
Eight maids a-milking,
Seven swans a-swimming,
Six geese a-laying,
Five gold rings,
Four calling birds,
Three French hens,
Two turtle doves
And a partridge in a pear tree.

The Christmas Story

In Nazareth, in Palestine, there lived a young woman called Mary. She was engaged to a man called Joseph, who was a carpenter. One day, to her astonishment, an angel appeared before her and told her that God was pleased with her. Seeing Mary's startled face, the angel spoke gently to her.

"Don't be afraid! God loves you. You are going to have a baby son and you must give Him the name Jesus. He will be great and He will be known as the Son of the Most High. God will give Him the kingdom of His ancestor, King David, and He will reign for ever."

"But I don't understand how this can happen," said Mary. The angel explained that the baby's father would be God Himself.

Mary trusted in God and she said, "I will do whatever He asks of me. Let it be just as you have said."

When he heard the news, Joseph was worried, but an angel appeared to him in a dream and told him that Mary's story was true. Mary and Joseph looked forward to the birth of this special baby.

In those days, Palestine was ruled by the Romans. The Roman Governor ordered that every man should go to his home town to be registered. Joseph was descended from King David, so Bethlehem was his home town. Even though Mary's baby would soon be born, she had to travel with Joseph to Bethlehem.

But Bethlehem was full of people who had come to register and none of the inns had any room. At last a kind innkeeper took pity on them and let Mary and Joseph stay in his stable. That night Mary's baby, Jesus, was born. Mary laid Him in a manger, on the hay left for the animals to eat.

On the hills around Bethlehem some shepherds were watching their sheep. Suddenly a bright light shone on them and a voice told them not to be afraid. "I have wonderful news for you and all people," it said. The voice told the shepherds of the birth of Jesus in the city of David. The trembling shepherds saw that the sky was filled with angels singing,

"Glory to God in the highest,
And on earth, peace. Goodwill to all men."

Then the angels disappeared and the shepherds were left looking up at the starry sky. At once they hurried down into Bethlehem and found their way to the stable. There they saw the baby Jesus, lying in the manger, and were filled with wonder.

Later other visitors came to see Mary's baby. They were wise men, who had come from the East following an unusual star that had appeared in the night sky. They knew that the star meant that a great King had been born. At first the wise men thought that the new

King would be born in a palace, and they visited King Herod in Jerusalem. But Herod knew nothing of Jesus and was alarmed to think that another leader would come to take his place. Secretly, he planned to kill this new baby but he smiled pleasantly at the wise men. "This is fascinating news. Please do come here on your way home and tell me whether you found the new King," he said.

The wise men promised and journeyed on, following the star. At last the star stopped above the stable where Jesus lay and the wise men went in to offer him gifts of gold, frankincense and myrrh.

God sent the wise men a dream, warning them not to visit Herod on their way home. Then Joseph, too, had a dream. An angel warned him to escape with Mary and Jesus into Egypt, where Herod could not find them.

So in the middle of the night, Joseph led his family out of Bethlehem and they began the long journey to safety.

Silent Night

Silent night, holy night,
All is calm, all is bright
Around yon Virgin Mother and Child,
Holy infant, so tender and mild.
Sleep in heavenly peace,
Sleep in heavenly peace.

Silent night, holy night,
Shepherds quake at the sight;
Glories stream from heaven afar,
Heavenly hosts sing hallelujah.
Christ, the Redeemer, is born,
Christ, the Redeemer, is born.

Silent night, holy night,
Son of God, Love's pure light;
Radiance beams from Thy holy face
With the dawn of redeeming grace,
Jesus, Lord, at Thy birth,
Jesus, Lord, at Thy birth.

The Little Match Girl

It was a cold and bleak New Year's Eve in the town. Snow was falling and the streets were darkening as wealthy people hurried home to their firesides.

But one little figure did not hurry with the rest. In a doorway crouched a poor little girl, trying to sell matches to buy herself a crust of bread to eat. No one wanted to stop as they walked quickly by. Some did not even see the shivering figure, with her bare feet and ragged clothes.

At last the streets began to empty and the lamplit windows beckoned home the last passers by. The little match girl huddled alone in her doorway, trying to keep warm. Across the street, through a lit window, she could see happy people sitting around a blazing fire, raising their glasses toasting the New Year.

Blue with cold, the little match girl struck one of her precious matches.

It seemed as though a glowing fireplace appeared before her. With a little cry, she stretched her frozen feet toward it, but in another second the match went out and the fire disappeared.

With shaking fingers, the little girl struck another match. Now it seemed as though she could see through the wall of the house opposite. There was a table piled high with good things to eat and drink. As she watched, a plate of delicious food seemed to float toward her. The little match girl eagerly stretched out her hands, but just as she could almost touch the plate, the match went out and the vision vanished into the darkness.

With tears on her cheeks, the little girl struck a third match. This time she seemed to be inside the room, sitting under a beautiful Christmas tree with sparkling, shimmering candles. As she looked up into the flames, it was as though the candles floated up into the sky to become stars. One star fell to earth in a shimmering arc.

"Some poor soul must be dying," whispered the little match girl. "I remember my dear grandmother, before she left me and went to heaven, telling me that a star falls as someone dies."

She lit another match and saw her grandmother bending over her and smiling.

"Oh grandmother," cried the little girl. "Don't leave me this time! Please take me with you so that I can stay with you for ever!"

At that the old lady tenderly gathered the little girl into her arms and carried her gently into the sky, to a better place among the stars.

The next morning passers by found the little match girl still curled in her doorway, a smile on her frozen lips.

"Poor little girl," they said. "She lit her matches to try to keep warm but she could not save herself."

They did not understand that the little match girl had found a far better home than any of them in which to celebrate her New Year.

Good King Wenceslas

Good King Wenceslas looked out
On the Feast of Stephen,
When the snow lay 'round about,
Deep and crisp and even;
Brightly shone the moon that night,
Though the frost was cruel,
When a poor man came in sight,
Gathering winter fuel.

"Hither, page, and stand by me,
If thou know'st it, telling,
Yonder peasant, who is he?
Where and what his dwelling?"
"Sire, he lives a good league hence,
Underneath the mountain,
Right against the forest fence,
By Saint Agnes' fountain.

"Bring me flesh and bring me wine,
Bring me pine logs hither;
Thou and I will see him dine,
When we bear them thither."
Page and monarch forth they went,
Forth they went together,
Through the rude wind's wild lament
And the bitter weather.

"Sire, the night is darker now,
And the wind blows stronger;
Fails my heart, I know not how,
I can go no longer."
"Mark my footsteps, good my page!
Tread thou in them boldly:
Thou shalt find the winter's rage
Freeze thy blood less coldly."

In his master's steps he trod,
Where the snow lay dinted;
Heat was in the very sod
Which the saint had printed.
Therefore, Christian men, be sure,
Wealth or rank possessing,
Ye who now will bless the poor,
Shall yourselves find blessing.

The Elves and the Shoemaker

Once upon a time a shoemaker and his wife lived above a small shoe shop. Although the shoemaker worked hard and made beautiful shoes of many kinds, they were very poor.

"I'm afraid we shall be bankrupt by Christmas, my dear," said the shoemaker to his wife, "unless a miracle happens."

One day the shoemaker found that he had only enough money left to buy leather to make one pair of shoes. He cut the leather out carefully and left the pieces on his workbench before going upstairs to bed.

The next morning, when the shoemaker went to his workbench, he could hardly believe his eyes. There on the bench where he had left the leather was the prettiest pair of shoes he had ever seen. He peered at them more closely. The stitches were neat and tiny. The shoes had been beautifully made. Still muttering in amazement, he put the shoes in his shop window.

That morning a very rich lady happened to be passing by. She saw the shoes in the window and immediately rushed inside.

"I simply *must* have those shoes!" she cried, and she bought them on the spot.

"Shoes like this are worth more than you are asking, my man," she declared. "Please take this extra payment as well!"

So that afternoon the shoemaker was able to buy leather for *two* pairs of shoes. Just as before, he cut out the leather and left it on his bench overnight.

The next morning the same extraordinary thing happened. Two pairs of beautifully made shoes were standing there. The shoemaker put them in his window and had sold them to a passing merchant before the morning was out.

And so it went on. Every day the shoemaker was able to buy more leather and cut out more shoes. Every morning, no matter how much work he had left the night before, he found rows of perfectly made shoes on his workbench. Soon the poor shoemaker and his wife were two of the wealthiest people in the town.

One night just before Christmas, the shoemaker's wife spoke to him. "We still don't know who is helping us in this way. Why don't we stay up tonight and hide in your workroom? Then we will see what happens."

So that night the shoemaker and his wife hid behind the counter and waited quietly. At midnight the door opened and two of the strangest little people came running in. They were elves, with bare feet and ragged clothes. They ran straight to the bench and began to work. In no time at all they had finished sewing shoes from the cut leather. Then they ran away as quickly as they had come.

The next morning the shoemaker said to his wife, "I've been thinking, my dear. Surely we should do something to thank those little men, but whatever could it be?"

"Didn't you notice how ragged their clothes were?" asked his wife. "And their feet were bare even in this cold weather. Let's make them some little clothes and shoes to wear."

The shoemaker thought this was an excellent idea. For a whole week he and his wife cut and sewed until, on Christmas Eve, they had finished at last. They wrapped up the little costumes and put them on the workbench. Then they hid once more to see what would happen.

At midnight the little elves ran in as before. But how surprised they were to see presents instead of leather on the workbench. Laughing and chattering, they opened the packages and were overjoyed with what they found inside. At once they put on their little suits and the tiny shoes and socks that the shoemaker and his wife had made. They danced around with happiness and sang in their tiny voices,

"We look so fine, as you can see,
We need no longer cobblers be!"

And with that they skipped out of the door.

The elves never did return to the shoemaker's shop but perhaps they had left some of their magic behind, for the shoemaker and his wife were happy and wealthy for the rest of their lives.

Jingle Bells

Dashing through the snow
In a one-horse open sleigh,
O'er the field we go,
Laughing all the way.
Bells on bobtail ring,
Making spirits bright.
What fun it is to laugh and sing
A sleighing song tonight!

Jingle, bells! Jingle, bells!
Jingle all the way!
Oh, what fun it is to ride
In a one-horse, open sleigh – hey!
Jingle, bells! Jingle, bells!
Jingle all the way!
Oh, what fun it is to ride
In a one-horse open sleigh!

You won't mind the cold,
The robe is thick and warm.
Snow falls on the road,
Silv'ring every form.
The woods are dark and still,
The horse is trotting fast,
He'll pull the sleigh around the hill
And home again at last.

The Best Present

"I want a *big* truck," said Charlotte, "and I want some more carriages for my train, and I want a big box of crayons, and I want…." The list went on for some time, so that Charlotte's mother, who was feeling quite tired, stopped listening very soon.

"Christmas is for giving as well, Charlie," she said. "I'm sure you'll have some nice presents, but you can't possibly have *everything* you want. Now I want to talk to you about something…."

"That's not fair," interrupted Charlotte. "Anyway, there are lots of things I want that I haven't said, like…."

Her mother put her hands over her ears and went to rest. Thank goodness it was Christmas Eve and the waiting would soon be over! Charlotte's dad was out in the town now, picking up the big present that they had planned for their daughter.

As it got dark outside, Charlotte's mother brought her some toast and cheese.

"Can't I have something *really* nice?" asked Charlotte. "There's lots of yummy food in the kitchen. I want...."

"Charlie, that's enough!" said her mother firmly. "I'm tired of hearing about what you want. The food is for tomorrow and it won't be a surprise if you have it today. Now sit down with me and listen. I really must tell you...."

But just then Charlotte's dad arrived home with a huge package. "No looking, Charlie!" he cried, as he staggered up the stairs with the enormous box. Charlotte's mother followed him but he laughed and said, "I'll wrap it up, love, you take it easy!"

"Can we play horses?" demanded Charlotte.

"Not now, Charlie. I don't really feel like it," said her mother, "and anyway, I still want to have a quiet talk with you."

But Charlotte didn't want to talk quietly. She wanted to run and jump and yell because that's just how she felt with Christmas coming – *tomorrow*!

Much, much later, after quite a lot of running and jumping and yelling with her dad, Charlotte went to bed at last.

"Now if you hear any rustling and bustling in the night, you MUST NOT open your door," smiled her dad. "Because it will be you-know-who, and he might take your presents back if you see him."

So Charlotte snuggled down and tried very hard to sleep. She did hear a lot of rustling and bustling and she thought she heard the doorbell ring, but in the end she drifted into a wonderful dream about reindeer and great big boxes with bows on them.

The next morning, very early, Charlotte ran into her parents' room and suddenly stood quite still with her mouth open wide in surprise.

"Oh Charlie!" laughed her mother. "I don't think I've ever known you to stand so quiet and still for so long! Come and look at *my* present. It came a bit earlier than I expected. Actually, it's a present for all of us, not just me."

"This is the best present I've ever had!" whispered Charlotte. She didn't even look at the big box with the bows that was waiting for her on the floor.

"Well, sweetheart," laughed her dad. "I think we've given Charlie a Christmas present she really wants at last. Perhaps we should have a new baby *every* year! Hey, what are you doing with that pillow? Ouch!"

The Night Before Christmas

'Twas the night before Christmas, when all through the house
Not a creature was stirring, not even a mouse;
The stockings were hung by the chimney with care,
In hopes that St. Nicholas soon would be there;
The children were nestled all snug in their beds,
While visions of sugarplums danced in their heads.

And mamma in her kerchief, and I in my cap,
Had just settled our brains for a long winter's nap;
When out on the lawn there arose such a clatter,
I sprang from the bed to see what was the matter.
Away to the window I flew like a flash,
Tore open the shutters and threw up the sash.

The moon, on the breast of the new-fallen snow,
Gave the luster of midday to objects below,
When what to my wondering eyes should appear,
But a miniature sleigh, and eight tiny reindeer,
With a little old driver, so lively and quick,
I knew in a moment it must be St. Nick.

More rapid than eagles his coursers they came,
And he whistled and shouted, and called them by name:
"Now, Dasher! Now, Dancer! Now, Prancer and Vixen!
On, Comet! On, Cupid! On, Donner and Blitzen!
To the top of the porch! To the top of the wall!
Now, dash away! Dash away! Dash away all!

As dry leaves that before the wild hurricane fly,
When they meet with an obstacle, mount to the sky;
So up to the housetop the coursers they flew,
With the sleigh full of toys, and St. Nicholas, too.

And then, in a twinkling, I heard on the roof
The prancing and pawing of each little hoof –
As I drew in my head, and was turning around,
Down the chimney St. Nicholas came with a bound.

He was dressed all in fur, from his head to his foot,
And his clothes were all tarnished with ashes and soot;
A bundle of toys he had flung on his back,
And he looked like a peddler just opening his pack.
His eyes – how they twinkled! His dimples, how merry!
His cheeks were like roses, his nose like a cherry!

His droll little mouth was drawn up like a bow,
And the beard of his chin was as white as the snow;
The stump of a pipe he held tight in his teeth,
And the smoke it encircled his head like a wreath;
He had a broad face and a little round belly
That shook, when he laughed, like a bowl full of jelly.

He was chubby and plump, a right jolly old elf,
And I laughed, when I saw him, in spite of myself;
A wink of his eye and a twist of his head,
Soon gave me to know I had nothing to dread;
He spoke not a word, but went straight to his work,
And filled all the stockings; then turned with a jerk,

And laying his finger aside of his nose,
And giving a nod, up the chimney he rose;
He sprang to his sleigh, to his team gave a whistle,
And away they all flew like the down of a thistle.
But I heard him exclaim, 'ere he drove out of sight,
"Merry Christmas to all, and to all a good night."

Clement C. Moore

Baboushka

Once there was an old woman called Baboushka who lived all by herself in a wooden hut in the forest. The nearest house was many miles away, so old Baboushka was used to looking after herself and keeping busy. She baked her own bread and sewed her own clothes. She swept her wooden floor and polished her few plates and pots. Although Baboushka was very poor, she was happy.

One winter's night, as Baboushka sat sewing by her fire, she heard voices approaching the hut through the thick snow. Baboushka hardly ever had visitors, so at once she threw some more sticks on the fire and put on some water to boil for tea. There came three knocks on the wooden door.

When Baboushka looked outside, she could hardly believe her eyes. On the doorstep stood three very fine and important looking men.

"Come in, come in. You are very welcome on such a cold night," said Baboushka, and the three strangers walked in. The first to enter was young and wore a long velvet cloak, trimmed with fur. The second was an older man, dressed very elegantly but tired from the journey. The third was a tall, handsome man, with gold jewels and a silk robe. They all took their seats by the fire.

As she busied herself making the tea and finding some food, Baboushka asked the strangers where they were going.

"That is uncertain," said the first man. "We are following a star that will lead us to the place where a new Prince has been born. We do not know where it will stop, but now the snow is so thick that we cannot see to follow it."

"Then you must rest here," said the old woman kindly. "Here is some strong, hot tea. But tell me, sirs, who is this new Prince that you are searching for?"

"He is a holy child," said the second man. "He is the Christ child, who will reign forever."

Baboushka's eyes widened as the third man showed her the precious gifts that had been brought for the new baby. "I wish I could see this holy child," she said.

"Then why not come with us?" the three men replied. "You are very welcome to join us in our search."

"No, no," said Baboushka, a little sadly. "I am too old to go on a journey now. But I do wish you luck on your travels."

Soon the snow eased a little and the three men set off once more. Baboushka watched them from the door of her hut until their glowing robes were lost among the trees. Then she went inside and got ready for bed.

All night long old Baboushka tossed and turned, thinking of the Christ child. As the sun rose in the morning, she made up her mind. "I *will* go," she said. "Yes, indeed, I will!" As quickly as she could she packed a bag of small toys for the new baby. They were simple things: an old doll, some wooden animals and a few pretty feathers and pebbles. Then she wrapped her shawl around her head and set off across the snow.

Poor Baboushka! She had waited too long. The footprints of the strangers had been covered with snow and she could not follow them. Everywhere she went, Baboushka asked if anyone had seen the three wise men.

"Who?" asked a farmer. "Of course not! No one travels in this weather!"

So Baboushka walked on. Some say that she is still searching high and low, looking for the Christ child. And if she meets children who are poor, or ill, or sad, she finds a little present in her sack for them in memory of the holy child.

I Saw Three Ships

I saw three ships come sailing in,
On Christmas Day, on Christmas Day,
I saw three ships come sailing in,
On Christmas Day in the morning.

And what was in those ships all three?
On Christmas Day, on Christmas Day,
And what was in those ships all three?
On Christmas Day in the morning.

Our Lord Jesus Christ and his lady,
On Christmas Day, on Christmas Day,
Our Lord Jesus Christ and his lady,
On Christmas Day in the morning.

Pray, whither sailed those ships all three?
On Christmas Day, on Christmas Day,
Pray, whither sailed those ships all three?
On Christmas Day in the morning.

Oh, they sailed into Bethlehem,
On Christmas Day, on Christmas Day,
Oh, they sailed into Bethlehem,
On Christmas Day in the morning.

Traditional carol

The Real Reindeer

Across the frozen wastes of the Arctic Circle, a brown shape moved slowly. It was a real reindeer, separated from his herd in a snow storm. Day and night he roamed across the ice, looking for food and hoping to see his family in the distance.

One night, as he gazed into the sky, the reindeer saw something strange flying toward him. With a crash, it landed on the snow a few yards away.

"Oops!" cried a cheerful voice. "Not so good that time! I must remember to allow for the wind speed." It was an odd kind of sleigh and it was pulled by some quite impressive reindeer. Out of the strange machine climbed a jolly old man in a red suit. "Yooohooo!" he called.

The reindeer looked over his shoulder, but there was no one there. "I mean *you*!" laughed the merry old man. "Need a job? One of my reindeer has left at short notice. You can see how it's affected our landings. How would you like to fill in for a bit? Earn some pocket money? See a bit of the world?"

The reindeer cleared his throat. "Er, well, the fact is…" he began.

"What's the trouble? Prior engagement?"

"No, no, it's just that I've never learned to, er, *fly*."

The old man was doubled up with laughter. "Don't worry," he said. "There's on-the-job training. Come on!"

So the reindeer took his place with the others. "Hurry up!" cried the man in red, climbing into the sleigh. "This is a particularly busy night for me! Are you ready? Three, two, one … lift off!"

And the next minute, the reindeer was flying with all the rest. He felt a bit wobbly when he looked down, but if he kept his eyes on the stars, he was fine.

All that night, the sleigh flew over towns and villages, delivering presents. Sometimes they would be dropped straight down chimneys or through windows, but often the old fellow had to get out and deliver them himself. "Wretched central heating," he muttered.

When the very last house had been visited, the old man pulled off his red hat. "Time to go home," he said. "I'm ready for a hot bath and a good, long sleep. I've just one more present to deliver first."

"Er … what about me?" asked the real reindeer. "How will I get home?"

"We'll drop you off on the way," answered the old man.

Very soon, the sleigh flew low over a snowy landscape once more. "Will this be okay?" asked the old man. "There seems to be a few reindeer here already. You don't mind, do you?"

"Mind? It's my *family*!" cried the reindeer joyfully. And he ran off to join them.

"Well, that's the last present delivered," chuckled Santa Claus.

"See you all next year!"

The Christmas Mouse

A horrible silence had fallen on the family gathered in the dining room. "Christmas is supposed to be fun," thought Jason gloomily. But there was Great Aunt Gladys with her mouth drawn in a thin line of disapproval – nothing that Jason's mother had served up for Christmas dinner had been suitable for her sensitive stomach to cope with – or so she claimed.

Next to her were Aunt Diana and Uncle Paul. They weren't speaking to each other because their car had broken down on the way over and they couldn't decide whose fault it was. Jason's sister Alison was sulking because her boyfriend Mark wasn't taking any notice of her. Mark just sat there silently.

Jason's mother was sitting by the door, exhausted from cooking and trying to make polite conversation at dinner. His dad was slumped fast asleep in a corner, still wearing an apron from what he considered his gigantic efforts clearing the table.

Jason couldn't bear it any longer. "Perhaps everyone would like to see my presents," he said.

Jason's mother was so tired that she almost agreed, but she remembered just in time. "*No!*" she yelled, waking up her husband. "*Not now, Jason!*" For Jason's presents had all been of the noisiest kind – a trumpet, a new radio and an electronic drum kit. "If there's something *quiet* you can bring, get that," she went on, smiling at him. It was just as well that someone was making an effort.

So Jason went to his room and looked around. He didn't even think about taking the scarf he'd been given by his grandma and he couldn't imagine showing his novelty boxer shorts to his great aunt. Then his eyes lit up as he carefully lifted his new white mouse, Snowy, from her box.

Nothing had changed down in the dining room. Jason walked across to Great Aunt Gladys, his eyes on his cupped hands. That was why he didn't see the stool that she was resting her feet on.

In the confusion that followed, Great Aunt Gladys scolded, Aunt Diana fussed and Jason's dad grumbled. But Jason didn't notice. "Where's Snowy?" he yelled over all the noise.

There was a silence for a moment. "What?" asked everyone at once.

"Snowy, my mouse," explained Jason.

"Aagh," shrieked Jason's sister, throwing herself into Mark's arms.

"I *love* mice," cried Great Aunt Gladys, crouching down on her hands and knees.

"I'll catch it in my bag," yelled Aunt Diana, emptying a great pile of extraordinary things from her huge black bag onto the floor.

"Everyone stand clear, we need teamwork," shouted Uncle Paul.

Only Jason's parents were silent. They exchanged looks and quietly disappeared into the hall.

Five minutes later the crisis was over, and the gloomy silence was gone, too.

Mark and Jason's sister were giggling together on the sofa.

Uncle Paul beamed at his wife. "That was a *brilliant* idea, using your bag!"

"I couldn't have done it if you hadn't organized everyone so well," she smiled back.

"All this activity has made me hungry," declared Great Aunt Gladys. "I wonder if any of that delicious dinner is left?"

Jason's mother and father peeped back around the door. "I'm going to give that mouse the biggest hunk of cheese it's ever seen," said Jason's dad. "Merry Christ*mouse*, everyone!"

The Holly and the Ivy

The holly and the ivy,
When they are both full grown,
Of all the trees that are in the wood,
The holly bears the crown.

Chorus:
The rising of the sun
And the running of the deer,
The playing of the merry organ,
Sweet singing in the choir.

The holly bears a berry,
As red as any blood,
And Mary bore sweet Jesus Christ
To do poor sinners good.

The holly bears a prickle,
As sharp as any thorn,
And Mary bore sweet Jesus Christ
On Christmas Day in the morn.

The holly bears a bark,
As bitter as any gall,
And Mary bore sweet Jesus Christ
For to redeem us all.

The Little Christmas Tree

Many years ago, deep in a forest, a little fir tree grew in a small clearing. All around it were enormous trees, their tops reaching up toward the sky. The big trees had been growing for more than twenty years, but the little tree had grown from a seed only four years before.

"I wonder if I shall ever be as tall as that," said the little tree to himself, looking up at the starlit sky.

One cold day a truck with lots of men in it came along the broad forest road. It was time for the big trees to be felled and taken to the sawmill to be made into timber. The men checked the trees and looked at their charts.

"Yes," said the foreman. "All these are ready to go – except this little one, of course. He's not worth bothering with."

The men roared off in their truck before dusk fell. That night the little tree felt very sad. "I am sorry that you are going to be cut down," he said to the big trees.

The trees rustled their branches soothingly. "Don't worry about us," they said. "Our tall, smooth trunks will be used to make houses and boats and all kinds of interesting things. There are exciting adventures ahead of us. But you are too small for anything. You will just be thrown away."

Then the little tree was even more sad. He gazed up at the night sky. "This is the last time that I shall be able to look up at the stars," he thought.

The next morning many big trucks and more men came along the forest road. Soon the air was full of the noise of chainsaws and the creaking, crashing sound as the big trees were felled. Their branches were trimmed off before their long, straight trunks were loaded onto trucks and hauled away.

The men worked hard all day. By the time that the first evening star appeared in the sky, only the little fir tree was left standing. He saw a man striding toward him. "Goodbye, star," he whispered.

But the man did not pull the little fir tree up and throw him on one side. He dug very carefully around the tree with a shovel and lifted him, with a ball of earth protecting his roots.

Then he put the little tree in his truck and drove to his home.

When the man stopped the truck outside the farmhouse where he lived, three little children ran out and clapped their hands. "You've brought the Christmas tree!" they cried. "It's a lovely one!"

"Yes," said their father. "We will put it in a pot and give it plenty of water. When Christmas is over, we will plant it in the garden, where it will grow into a big tree and remind us of our happy Christmas."

So the little tree had his wish after all. Today he stands, tall and strong, in a field near the farmhouse, and at night his topmost branches almost seem to touch the stars.

We Three Kings

We three Kings of Orient are,
Bearing gifts we traverse afar,
Field and fountain, moor and mountain,
Following yonder star.

Chorus: Oh, star of wonder,
Star of night,
Star with royal beauty bright,
Westward leading, still proceeding,
Guide us to Thy perfect light.

MELCHIOR: Born a King on Bethlehem plain,
Gold I bring, to crown Him again,
King for ever, ceasing never,
Over us all to reign.

CASPAR: Frankincense to offer have I;
Incense owns a Deity nigh:
Prayer and praising, all men raising,
Worship Him, God most high.

BALTHAZAR: Myrrh is mine; its bitter perfume
Breathes a life of gathering gloom;
Sorrowing, sighing, bleeding, dying,
Sealed in a stone-cold tomb.

Glorious now behold Him arise,
King, and God, and sacrifice!
Heaven sings hallelujah,
Hallelujah the earth replies.

The Runaway Present

It was Christmas Eve and all the Christmas presents were piled up under the tree. There were big ones and small ones, long thin ones and round fat ones.

The clock struck twelve in the quiet room. There was an air of excitement all through the house as Christmas morning drew near. But suddenly, from the pile of presents, there came a bustling, rustling sound and some of the presents began to move slightly. The movements became more vigorous and a little voice could be heard. "Let me through! Excuse me! Please let me through!"

At last a small present, wrapped in red and green paper, with a big blue bow on the top, struggled out of the pile. As soon as it was free, it scuttled across the room on its short legs.

Out into the hall ran the little present and up to the front door. Then it jumped through the cat flap and fell onto the mat outside, much to the astonishment of Fluffy the cat who was just coming in.

The little present didn't stop. It ran off down the path as fast as its legs would carry it, leaving tiny footprints in the snow. Over the road it went, before setting off across the fields in the moonlight.

All night long, the little present kept running. If you listened carefully, you could hear it puffing and panting and muttering to itself. "Oh, I must get there. I really must get there." An owl sitting in an old oak tree looked down with interest on the hurrying present below. Silently, he swooped down and picked up the present in his beak, carrying it back to his branch to examine it. Several other young owls came to look as well.

Balanced precariously on the branch, the little present was frightened half out of its wits. "Please don't eat me," it cried. "Oh please don't eat me. I wouldn't taste good, honestly I wouldn't. And I'm in a hurry you see."

"Too whoo!" said the owl. "Where to?"

"I got mixed up in the pile of presents under the Christmas tree but really I should have been sent to the children's granny in the next town. She'll be so disappointed if I don't arrive. I really must try to get there by myself."

"Too whoo!" said the owl. "Well, flutter my feathers, that's the strangest story I've ever heard. But perhaps I can help. If you give me directions, I'll carry you into town. It will be much quicker if I fly. You'd never get there with your short little legs."

The present was a bit offended by the comment about his legs, but he was grateful to the owl. "Just be careful with your sharp beak," he said.

So the owl flew silently off through the trees, carrying the present in his mouth. Several little birds nearly fell off their perches at the sight.

As they neared the town, the little present became more sure of the way. "Left here, right there," he cried. "Watch out for that church steeple!" Soon they arrived at the children's granny's house. "Too whoo! But what will you do?" asked the owl.

"Actually," said the present proudly. "I'm rather good with cat flaps. Just watch!"

"Wait!" said the owl. "Before you go in, please show me what's inside you. I thought I heard ticking as we flew along, and then I thought I heard rattling, and then I thought I heard a jingling sound. What are you?"

"I'm surprised at you," said the present with dignity. "Can't a present have a little privacy? If you think I'm getting undressed on this doorstep, you are very much mistaken."

So the owl never did know what was inside the present and neither do we. But when you are unwrapping your presents next Christmas, look very carefully to see if one of them is a little bit out of breath, for that will be a very special present indeed.

The Christmas Carol Mystery

"It's a mystery," said Vikky, "and someone must find out their secret."

She was talking about Christmas carols. Every year two groups of singers went around the town, collecting money for charity. And every year the group from St. Mary's Church Choir, who sang like angels and walked for miles to visit even the most distant homes, collected less money than the group from the Youth Club. The Youth Club singers were made up of some of the naughtiest children in the town. Vikky was sure that they couldn't sing half so well as her group. So how did they collect so much money?

"What we need," commented Janine, "is a spy! One of us should go around with the Youth Club and see what they do."

"That won't work," said another voice. "They know all of us."

But Vikky had had an idea. "My cousin Jemima is coming to stay for Christmas," she said. "She can go around with the Youth Club and report back to us."

So that was what happened. Jemima went along to the Youth Club and volunteered.

"When is the practice?" she asked a boy who was trying to pour super glue into his friend's bicycle lock.

"Practice?" said the boy. "There isn't one. We've just got natural talent. See you at seven thirty on Thursday."

"Shall I bring a book of carols?" asked Jemima.

"If you like," said the boy. "But you won't really need it."

Jemima reported back to the team from St. Mary's. "I think you should go out singing on Wednesday night," she said. "Before the Youth Club have a chance to do it first."

The St. Mary's Choir spent all Wednesday evening trudging the streets, calling at every house. Many people said how well they sang and some gave them hot drinks or food. They collected a lot of money, too.

On Thursday, Jemima set off to join the Youth Club group. "We only go to the biggest houses," explained their leader, Gary. "It doesn't take very long." Jemima grew more and more puzzled, as they walked up the drive to Darke Hall.

"All right team," said Gary, as they reached the imposing front door. "One, two, three … Jingle bells, jingle bells…"

And there began the most awful noise that Jemima had ever heard. Gary persevered with "Jingle Bells" but he had forgotten most of the words. Matthew also had a good try at it but he was attempting to sing it to the tune of "Silent Night". Karen had started off with "In the Bleak Midwinter" because it was the only carol she could remember with snow in it. The twins, Jake and James, were both singing "We Wish You a Merry Christmas" but they hadn't started together and certainly didn't finish together.

Before Jemima could open her mouth, a face appeared at the door and the deafening noise raggedly stopped. "Another carol, sir?" asked Gary politely.

"No, no!" cried the man, thrusting money at the choir. "Please, save yourselves for the next house."

And so it went on. Time and again, the Youth Club were paid handsomely to go *anywhere* else! After a while Jemima began to enjoy herself.

That night, Vikky and the others waited anxiously for news of their rivals. Jemima thought for a minute. "You couldn't possibly do what they do," she said truthfully, "and there's plenty of room for both of you in town. But I don't think you'll *ever* collect so much as them." And that was all she would say.

So St. Mary's Choir never did solve the Christmas carol mystery. You won't tell them, will you?

The Christmas Snowman

"It's not as though I'll be here very long," muttered the snowman. "It's the same every year. Those children take ages to make me. They give me an old hat and a moth-eaten scarf and think they can forget about me. Along comes that man in the red coat and the beard and yours truly might never exist. It's awful."

The next day the snowman wasn't any happier. "I can feel a thaw in the air," he grumbled. "Here we go again. Three days of cold weather and the sun comes out! Typical! Next thing we know, my toes will start to melt and then it'll be drip, drip, drip, until this stupid hat is the only thing that's left."

But the sun went in again and that night there was a sharp frost. Was the snowman happy? Not one bit!

"This is no good," he moaned. "It's too cold for the kids to come out and play, so I'm all on my own.

Except for these wretched birds, of course. Look here, mate, if you do what I think you're about to do on my hat, you'll be sorry."

The snowman was still grumbling that night when there was a swooshing and wooshing in the sky and a sleigh pulled by reindeer swooped down onto the snow.

"Oh no," said the snowman gloomily. "It's that man in red. I'm surprised all that wooshing didn't melt me. He's coming over. Now what on earth does *he* want?"

The old man strolled up to the snowman. "How's it going?" he asked. The snowman was about to begin on his usual moaning and groaning but something in the man's cheery face and twinkling eyes stopped him.

"It's not bad," he said. "I've known worse years. But everyone forgets about me once you have come."

"Is that so?" said the merry old man. "Well, I think I can fix that. Why don't you look after this bag of presents for me? I'll leave the children a note to say that you've got it."

"It'll be safe with me, sir," said the snowman, proud to have a *real* job at last. He didn't close his eyes all night but guarded the bag carefully.

In the morning all the children from the house across the street came running over the snow to find their presents. Their dad came too with his video camera and filmed them opening their gifts.

"Fame at last!" thought the snowman, as the
camera zoomed in for a close-up. "Yes, this *is* my best
side. Is my hat on straight?"

Later, when the children had carried their presents
home, the snowman had time to think about all the
exciting things that had happened.

"That man in red never stays around long enough
to become a star like me," he thought. "The children
never have a chance to see him at all. Poor guy. Is that
you, bird? Why don't you sit on my hat? It'll be warmer
for your feet."

So that was how a grumpy snowman became a jolly
snowman. Nowadays, if there's not enough snow at
Christmas to build him, the children miss him as
much as they would the old man in red.

Well, almost.

In the Bleak Midwinter

In the bleak midwinter
Frosty wind made moan,
Earth stood hard as iron,
Water like a stone;
Snow had fallen, snow on snow,
Snow on snow,
In the bleak midwinter,
Long ago.

Our God, heaven cannot hold Him
Nor earth sustain;
Heaven and earth shall flee away
When he comes to reign.
In the bleak midwinter
A stable-place sufficed
The Lord God Almighty,
Jesus Christ.

What can I give him?
Poor as I am?
If I were a shepherd,
I would bring a lamb;
If I were a wise man
I would do my part;
Yet what I can I give him –
Give my heart.

Christina Rosetti

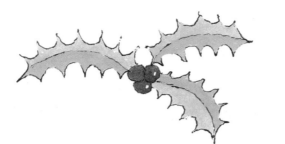

Mrs. Muddle's Present Puzzle

One September morning, Mrs. Muddle said to herself, "I will *not* get into the kind of muddle I did last Christmas. I will do my Christmas shopping *early* so that there are no last-minute panics. Advance planning is the secret."

She set off for the shops and spent all day busily running around the town, buying presents for her friends and family. At last she staggered home, loaded with bags, and collapsed on her sofa.

"I am *exhausted*," said Mrs. Muddle, "but I won't stop until every present is wrapped up and put safely away." So Mrs. Muddle wrapped up the train set she had bought for her nephew Jimmy and the bright wool scarf and hat she had bought for her brother Sam. Then she wrapped up the cookbook for stern Aunt Susan and the sensible socks for Great Uncle Harry, the roller skates for little Susie and the microscope for Susie's big brother Tom.

Everything looked very Christmassy. Mrs. Muddle hid the presents under the bed.

On Christmas Eve, Mrs. Muddle decided that it was time to deliver her presents. She pulled out the bag and emptied the packages onto the table. "Oh no! I have made a muddle after all!" she said to herself. "I didn't put any labels on the parcels and now I can't remember which is which." There really wasn't time to undo the presents and wrap them up again, so Mrs. Muddle did her best to guess what each one contained. "I do hope I've got this right," thought Mrs. Muddle, as she set off to make her Christmas deliveries.

Christmas morning was bright and clear. Mrs. Muddle looked out of her window and saw an extraordinary sight. Great Uncle Harry was roller-skating down the road. He waved as he sped past. "Can't stop now – don't know how! Best present I've had in years! Thank you!"

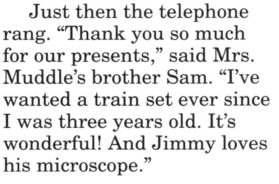

"Oh my goodness," said Mrs. Muddle. "Then who has got the sensible socks?"

A second later little Susie came speeding past on her own pair of roller skates. "My aunty gave them to me," she yelled. "And these socks are great! It doesn't hurt at all when I fall over! Thank you!"

Just then the telephone rang. "Thank you so much for our presents," said Mrs. Muddle's brother Sam. "I've wanted a train set ever since I was three years old. It's wonderful! And Jimmy loves his microscope."

Mrs. Muddle was beginning to feel rather confused, when there was a knock at the door. Stern Aunt Susan beamed out from her bright wool hat and scarf. "Thank you so much for my presents," she said. "I *love* them. Everyone always gives me such *sensible* things. These are such *fun*!"

"Well, well," said Mrs. Muddle. "Almost everyone seems happy. Now let me think. What can little Susie's brother Tom have got?"

Before she had time to work it out, Tom was standing on the doorstep. "I've made you some cookies from my cookbook," he smiled. "They look a bit funny, but they taste good! It's a great present!"

Mrs. Muddle sat down with a cup of coffee and one of Tom's cookies. "This has been the *most* muddled and *most* successful Christmas ever. I *knew* advance planning was the answer!"

The First Noel

The first Noel the angels did say
Was to certain poor shepherds in fields as they lay;
In fields where they lay, keeping their sheep,
On a cold winter's night that was so deep.

Chorus: Noel, Noel, Noel, Noel,
                     Born is the King of Israel!

They lookèd up and saw a star,
Shining in the East, beyond them far;
And to the earth it gave great light,
And so it continued both day and night.

Chorus: Noel, Noel, Noel, Noel,
                     Born is the King of Israel!

And by the light of that same star,
Three wise men came from country far;
To seek for a King was their intent,
And to follow the star wherever it went.

Chorus: Noel, Noel, Noel, Noel,
                     Born is the King of Israel!

This star drew nigh to the north-west;
O'er Bethlehem it took its rest,
And there it did both stop and stay
Right over the place where Jesus lay.

Chorus: Noel, Noel, Noel, Noel,
      Born is the King of Israel!

So let us all with one accord
Sing praises to our heavenly Lord,
That hath made heaven and earth of naught,
And with His blood mankind hath bought.

Chorus: Noel, Noel, Noel, Noel,
      Born is the King of Israel!

And if we in our time shall do well,
We shall be free of death and hell;
For God hath prepared for us all
A resting place in general.

Chorus: Noel, Noel, Noel, Noel,
      Born is the King of Israel!

The Full House

"I don't know how we're going to manage this Christmas," said Mrs. Moore. "We're going to be full to the rafters."

"Yes, dear," said her husband, without thinking. He was buried deep in his paper and thought it was easiest not to argue.

"Well, I had to invite your sister Maggie and her children when I heard that her new kitchen wouldn't be ready in time," explained Mrs. Moore. "You can't have Christmas without a kitchen."

"Quite right," said Mr. Moore vaguely. "I've just got a few things to do in the tool shed...."

A couple of days later, Mr. Moore's quiet time with the newspaper was interrupted again. "I really don't know where I'm going to put them all," he heard his wife say. "But I couldn't let Jimmy and his mother stay in that drafty old house over Christmas."

"Is there no peace?" thought Mr. Moore, behind his paper. "You know best about these things, dear. I'll be in the tool shed if you want me," he said.

Mr. and Mrs. Moore's house was not very big, and on Christmas Eve, when he came in from the quiet of his tool shed, Mr. Moore began to think that perhaps he should have paid more attention before. He walked into the living room as he usually did and fell flat on his face. Mrs. Moore had pulled out the sofabed for Jimmy and his mother to sleep on.

"Honestly, George," she said, when she had picked him up, "I did *tell* you we would be full over Christmas."

Upstairs, Mr. Moore had another surprise. His nightshirt was laid on a sleeping bag on the landing. "Yes, we're going to sleep out here," explained his wife. "I've given our room to Maggie and the children. It will still be a tight squeeze for them. After all, it's only for one night and we don't need so much room."

"But people will walk on us in the night," moaned Mr. Moore.

"I've thought of that," said Mrs. Moore, cheerfully. "We'll leave the light on so that they can see the way to the bathroom."

"I can't sleep with the light on," protested her husband.

"Don't make such a fuss," said Mrs. Moore. "You'll enjoy yourself."

Mr. Moore thought this was highly unlikely. "There is to be no more of this taking in of waifs and strays," he said to his wife, "even at Christmas."

In fact Mr. Moore did quite enjoy himself that evening, with so many people for supper. There were not enough chairs but somehow that didn't seem to matter. Everyone was happy and laughing. Perhaps it was nice to have a full house after all.

Just as everyone was getting ready for bed, the doorbell rang. "Whoever can that be?" said Mrs. Moore, going downstairs.

On the doorstep stood a young woman with a tiny baby. "I'm so sorry to disturb you," she said, "but someone told me that you sometimes help people in difficulties. I need somewhere to stay, just for tonight. There was a fire in my street today and everything at home is wet from the firefighters' hoses. We don't need much – the floor will be fine."

"I'm sorry," said Mrs. Moore, "but I just have no room at all."

"Nonsense," said a voice behind her. It was Mr. Moore. "Of course you can stay," he said. "It is Christmas after all. We'll just have to do a little reorganizing."

Mrs. Moore smiled to herself. Her husband was goodhearted really. But she couldn't think how they were going to manage.

Later that night, Mr. Moore sighed contentedly. "This is really surprisingly comfortable," he said. "Don't you think so, my dear?"

Mrs. Moore chuckled. "Well, it's a place you've always been particularly fond of," she said. "And it's a lot quieter than the house! Shall I turn the light off?"

"By all means," said Mr. Moore, tucked up in his tool shed. "Merry Christmas!"

Teddy Bear Christmas

On Christmas Eve teddy bears find it just as hard to go to sleep as children do. Their bright little eyes just will not close. Of course, *some* teddy bears, who have eaten a very big supper, may settle down to sleep. But in no time at all, an excited little bear will come along to disturb them.

One Christmas Eve not long ago, Grandfather Bear tried everything he could think of to persuade the little ones to go to bed.

"If you don't go to sleep, a Very Important Visitor might not come *at all*," he warned. He tucked the little bears into bed and crept away. Before he even reached the door, he heard a little voice. "Is it morning yet?"

Grandfather Bear sighed. He knew that teddy bears need their sleep, so he said goodnight and shut the bedroom door firmly behind him.

Grandfather Bear snuggled down into his own comfortable bed and switched off the light.

But *could* Grandfather Bear fall asleep? He could not! "Really I am a foolish old bear," he said to himself. "How silly to be excited about Christmas at *my* age."

No matter how hard he tried, he could *not* go to sleep.

And what were those squeaking, scuffling noises at the door? Grandfather Bear smiled to himself. "All right you bad little teddy bears," he called. "You can come in and I'll read you a story until you feel sleepy."

Grandfather Bear switched on the light and opened his special book of Teddy Bear stories and what do you think he read? "On Christmas Eve teddy bears find it just as hard to go to sleep as children do...."

We Wish You a Merry Christmas

We wish you a Merry Christmas,
We wish you a Merry Christmas,
We wish you a Merry Christmas
And a Happy New Year!

Glad tidings we bring
To you and your kin.
We wish you a Merry Christmas,
And a Happy New Year.

Oh, bring us some Christmas pudding,
Oh, bring us some Christmas pudding,
Oh, bring us some Christmas pudding
And a glass of good cheer!

We won't go until we get some,
We won't go until we get some,
We won't go until we get some
So bring it right here!

We wish you a Merry Christmas,
We wish you a Merry Christmas,
We wish you a Merry Christmas
And a Happy New Year!